I AM ME AND YOU ARE YOU

AUTHOR: JILLIA WEINBERGER

Dedicated by Jason and Asher Weinberger in loving memory of Jillia and her dream

I AM ME AND YOU ARE YOU

TO ASHER, THE SWEETEST BOY IN THE WORLD.

I KNOW YOU WILL CONTINUE TO SPREAD LOVE AND

KINDNESS TO ALL THE BEAUTIFUL AND UNIQUE PEOPLE

YOU MEET ALONG YOUR AMAZING LIFE JOURNEY.

I AM ME AND YOU ARE YOU

THIS BOOK BELONGS TO

I am me and you are you.

I am special and you are too.

Everyone is special in their own way.

Sometimes we have friends that are bigger than us. Sometimes we have friends that are smaller than us.

Some of our friends celebrate the same holidays as us. Some of our friends celebrate different holidays.

Sometimes our friends have families that look like ours. Sometimes there are families that look different.

Sometimes our friends move around using two legs. Sometimes our friends move around using a special chair.

Sometimes our friends have the same interests as us.

Sometimes our friends prefer to do something different.

I am me and you are you.

I am beautiful and you are too.

We are all beautiful in our own way.

I AM ME AND YOU ARE YOU

I AM ME AND YOU ARE YOU

CONTACT US

EMAIL: JILLIA.WEINB@GMAIL.COM

INSTAGRAM: MOMMYLIFEFUN

Made in the USA
Middletown, DE
20 October 2022

13071679R00015